2 **EITHER**

(a) Write a rhythm on one note, with time signature and bar-lines, to fit these w
Write each syllable under the note or notes to which it applies.

> A little cock sparrow sat on a green tree,
> and he chirruped, he chirruped, so merry was he. *Anon.*

Rhythm ____

Words ....

Rhythm ____

Words ....

OR

(b) Write a complete four-bar rhythm in $\frac{4}{4}$ time using the given opening.

3 Look at this melody by Koechlin and then answer the questions that follow.

Assez animé

10

(a) (i) Giving the meaning of:

Assez .... (2)

animé .... (2)

(ii) Give the technical names (e.g. tonic, dominant) of the two notes in bar 6 marked **X** and **Y**.
The key is A major.

X .... (2)

Y .... (2)

(iii) A square bracket ( ) has been drawn over the first phrase.
Mark all the other phrases in the same way. (2)

10

(b) (i) Name the major key that uses all the notes of bars 9–10. Key: .... major. (2)

(ii) How many demisemiquavers (32nd notes) is the last note of the melody worth? .... (2)

(iii) How many times does the rhythm occur? .... (2)

(iv) Rewrite bars 10–12 using notes of *twice the value*.
Remember to include the new time signature.

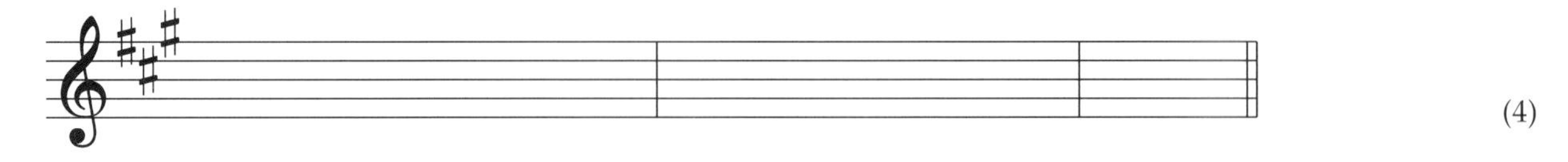

(4)

(c) (i) Name two standard orchestral instruments, one string and one woodwind, which normally use the treble clef, that could play this melody so that it sounds at the same pitch.

10

String .... (2)

Woodwind .... (2)

(ii) Answer TRUE or FALSE to each of the following statements:

A cellist may sometimes be asked to play 'con sord.'. .... (2)

A bassoonist may sometimes be asked to play 'pizzicato'. .... (2)

(iii) Name a standard orchestral brass instrument that normally uses the bass clef.

.... (2)

4 (a) Write the key signature of B major and then one octave **ascending** of that scale. Use semibreves (whole notes) and begin on the tonic.

10

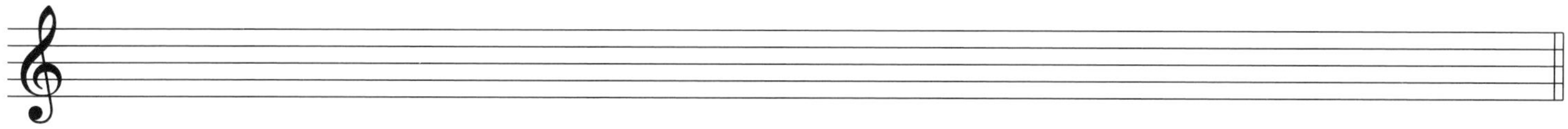

(b) Add the correct clef and any necessary sharps or flats to these notes to make the scale of F **harmonic** minor. Do *not* use a key signature.

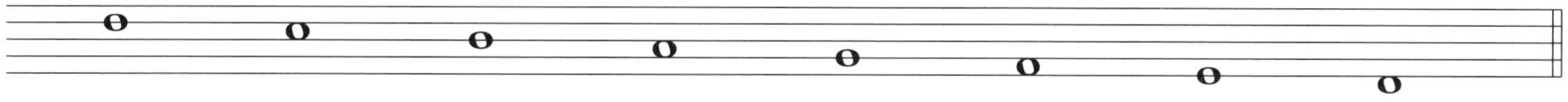

5 Describe fully (e.g. major 2nd, perfect 8ve) each of the numbered and bracketed melodic intervals in this extract.

10

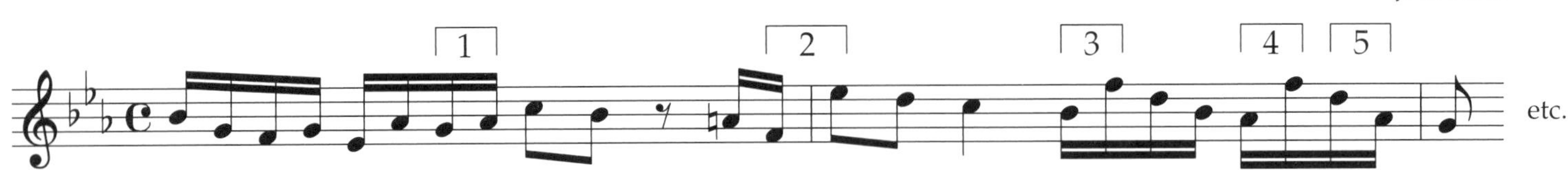

Intervals:

1 ....

2 ....

3 ....

4 ....

5 ....

6 Add the correct rest(s) at the places marked * to make each bar complete.

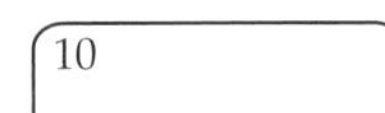

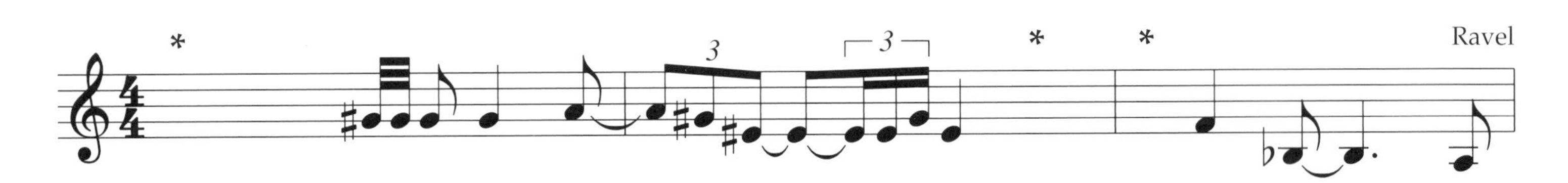

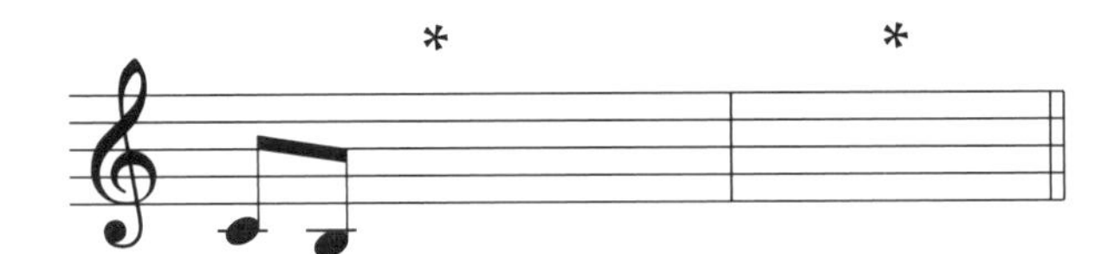

7 (a) Name each of the numbered chords as tonic (I), subdominant (IV) or dominant (V). The key is E♭ major.

15

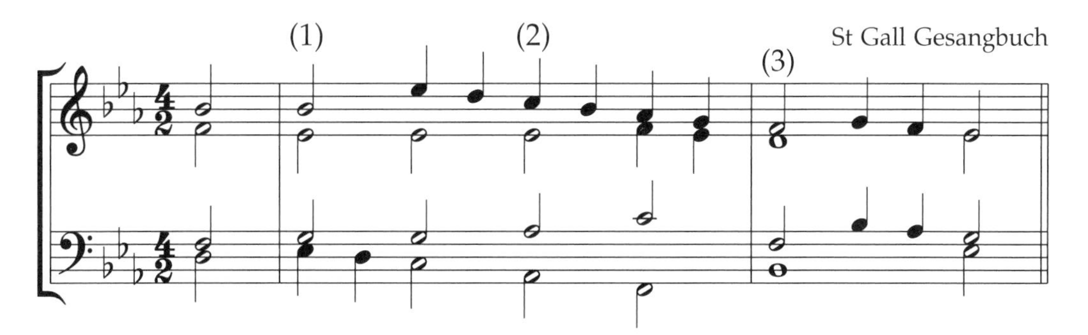

Chord:

(1) ....

(2) ....

(3) .... (9)

(b) Write the key signatures and triads named below.

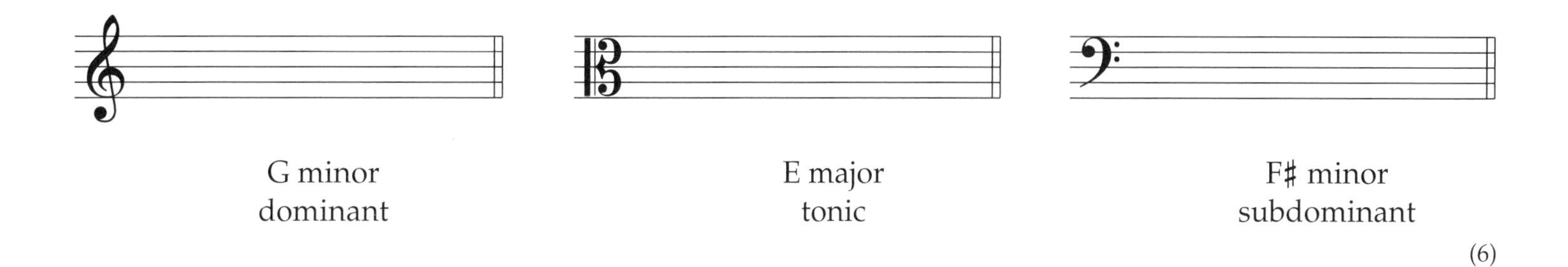

(6)

Theory Paper Grade 4 2014 B

Duration 2 hours

This paper contains SEVEN questions, ALL of which should be answered.
Write your answers on this paper – no others will be accepted.
Answers must be written clearly and neatly – otherwise marks may be lost.

TOTAL MARKS 100

15

1 Look at this melody by Mendelssohn, and then answer the questions below.

(a) Give the meaning of ***mf***. .... (1)

(b) Give the technical name (e.g. tonic, supertonic) of the first note of the melody. The key is G major. .... (2)

(c) Underline one word from the list below that has a similar meaning to **Allegro**.

douce *vite* *ralentir* *modéré* (2)

(d) Name the ornament used in bar 3. .... (2)

(e) Draw a circle around three notes next to each other that form the tonic triad of G major. (2)

(f) Rewrite bar 3, *without the ornament*, in simple time but without changing the rhythmic effect. Remember to include the new time signature.

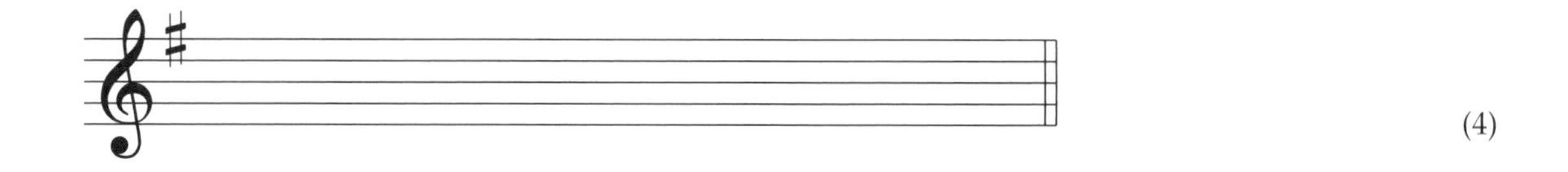

(4)

(g) Write as a breve (double whole-note) an enharmonic equivalent of the first note in bar 2.

(2)

2 EITHER 10

(a) Write a rhythm on one note, with time signature and bar-lines, to fit these words.
Write each syllable under the note or notes to which it applies.

> The wrinkled sea beneath him crawls;
> He watches from his mountain walls. *Alfred, Lord Tennyson*

Rhythm ______________________________

Words ....

Rhythm ______________________________

Words ....

OR

(b) Write a complete four-bar rhythm in $\frac{4}{2}$ time using the given opening.

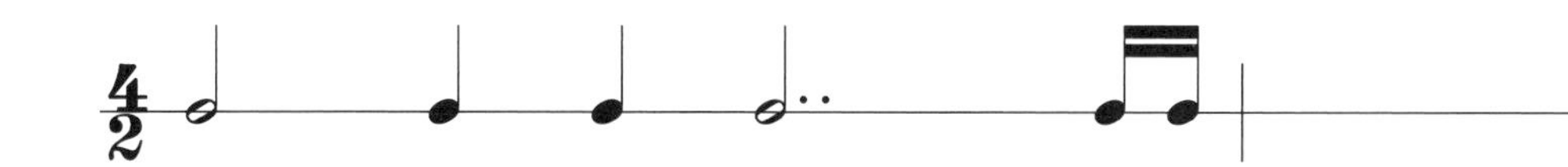

3 Look at this extract, which is adapted from a piece by Koechlin, and then answer the questions that follow.

10

(a) (i) Give the meaning of:

con moto .... (2)

maestoso .... (2)

en dehors (bar 3) .... (2)

(ii) Add the correct rest(s) at the place marked * to complete the last bar. (2)

(iii) How many demisemiquavers (32nd notes) are the tied notes in bar 2 worth in total? .... (2)

10

(b) (i) Rewrite the first two notes in bar 3 so that they sound at the same pitch, but using the alto clef. Remember to put in the clef sign and key signature.

(4)

(ii) Name the *major* key that uses all the notes in bars 1–2. Key: .... major. (2)

(iii) Which other key has the same key signature as the key you named in (ii) above? .... (2)

(iv) Answer TRUE or FALSE to the following statement:

There are four melodic intervals of a perfect 8ve in this melody. .... (2)

(c) (i) Name a standard orchestral brass instrument, which normally uses the bass clef, that could play bars 1–2 of this melody so that it sounds at the same pitch.

10

.... (2)

(ii) Name a *different* family of standard orchestral instruments and state its highest-sounding member.

Family .... Instrument .... (4)

(iii) Underline *two* instruments from the list below that might be played 'pizzicato'.

oboe viola cymbals double bass (4)

4 (a) Add all necessary sharp, flat or natural signs to the notes that need them to make a chromatic scale beginning on the given note.

10

(b) Write the key signature of C♯ minor and then one octave of its **descending melodic** minor scale. Use semibreves (whole notes), begin on the tonic and remember to include any necessary additional sharp, flat or natural signs.

5 Rewrite this melody using notes and rests of *twice the value*.
Remember to include the new time signature.

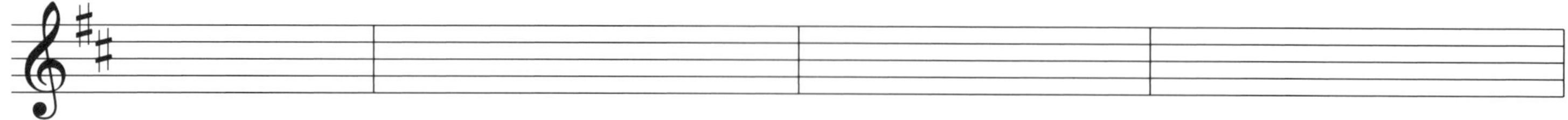

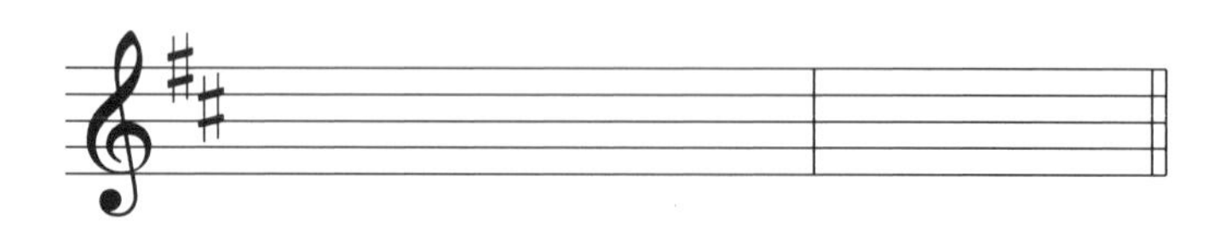

6 (a) Rewrite these treble clef notes at the same pitch but using the alto clef.

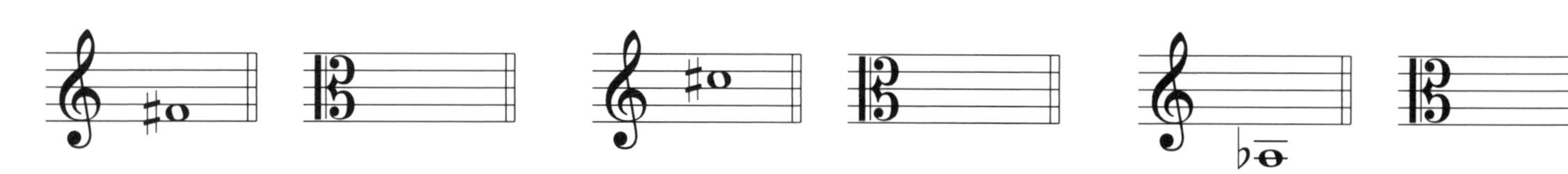

(b) Rewrite these alto clef notes at the same pitch but using the bass clef.

7 (a) Name each of the numbered chords as tonic (I), subdominant (IV) or dominant (V). The key is G major.

15

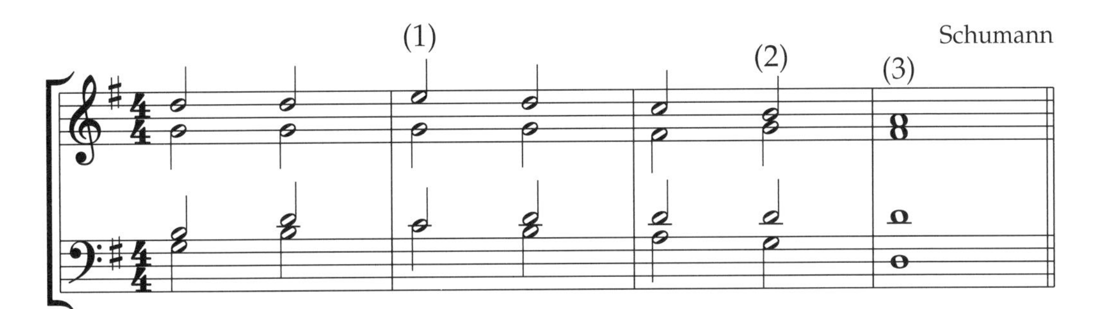

Chord:

(1) ....

(2) ....

(3) .... (9)

(b) Identify these triads by naming the key and describing them as tonic (I), subdominant (IV) or dominant (V).

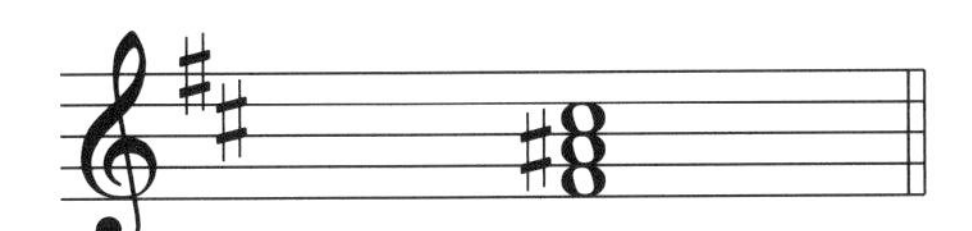

Key ....

Triad ....

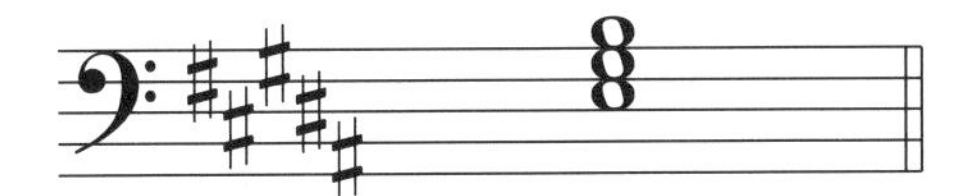

Key ....

Triad ....

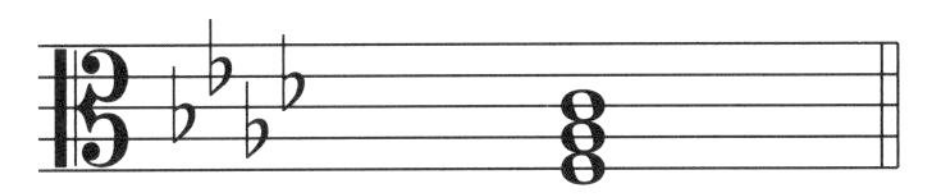

Key ....

Triad ....

(6)

Theory Paper Grade 4 2014 C

Duration 2 hours

This paper contains SEVEN questions, ALL of which should be answered.
Write your answers on this paper – no others will be accepted.
Answers must be written clearly and neatly – otherwise marks may be lost.

TOTAL MARKS 100

1 Look at this melody by Fauré and then answer the questions below.

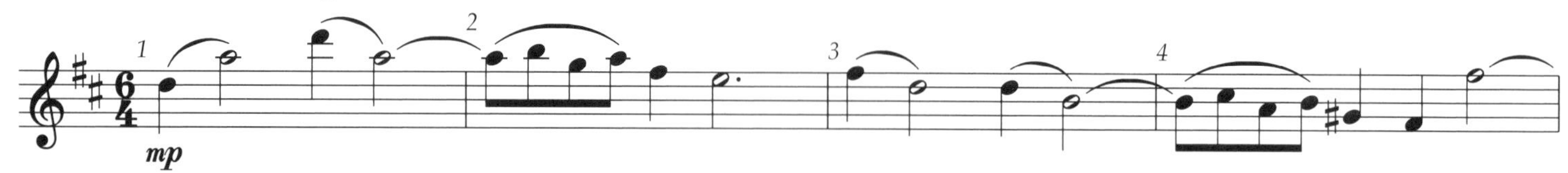

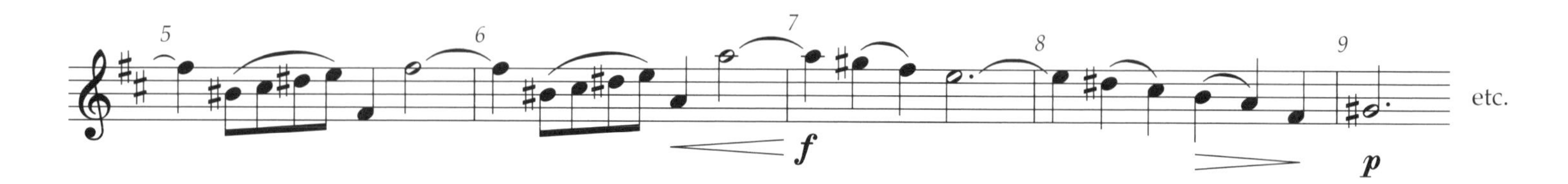

(a) Give the meaning of tranquillo. .... (2)

(b) Describe the time signature as: simple or compound .... (1)

duple, triple or quadruple .... (1)

(c) Name one similarity and one difference between bar 5 and bar 6.

Similarity .... (1)

Difference .... (1)

(d) Rewrite the last note of the melody so that it sounds at the same pitch, but using the alto clef. Remember to put in the clef sign and key signature.

(3)

(e) Rewrite bars 1–2 using notes of *half the value*. Remember to include the new time signature.

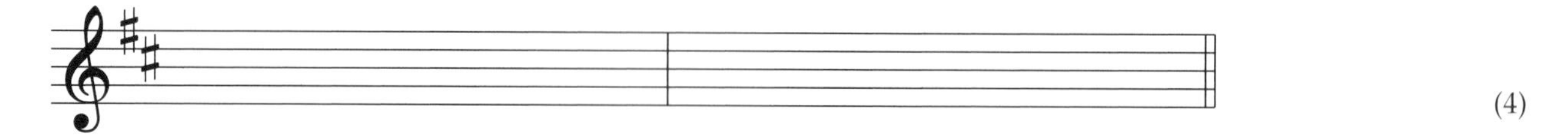

(4)

(f) How many pairs of tied notes appear in the melody? .... (2)

2 EITHER

10

(a) Write a rhythm on one note, with time signature and bar-lines, to fit these words.
Write each syllable under the note or notes to which it applies.

She's the daughter of the breeze,
She's the darling of the seas. *Sir Henry Newbolt*

Rhythm ______________________________

Words ....

Rhythm ______________________________

Words ....

OR

(b) Write a complete four-bar rhythm in $\frac{12}{8}$ time using the given opening.
Remember to complete the first bar.

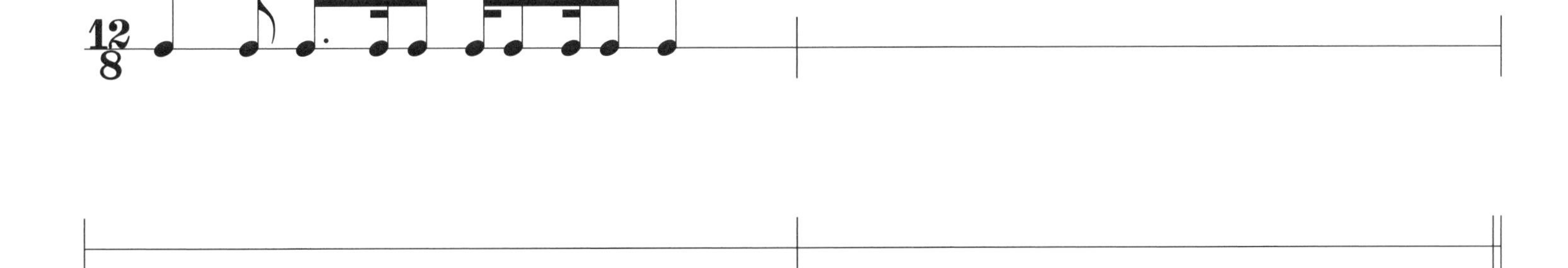

3 Look at this melody by d'Indy and then answer the questions that follow.

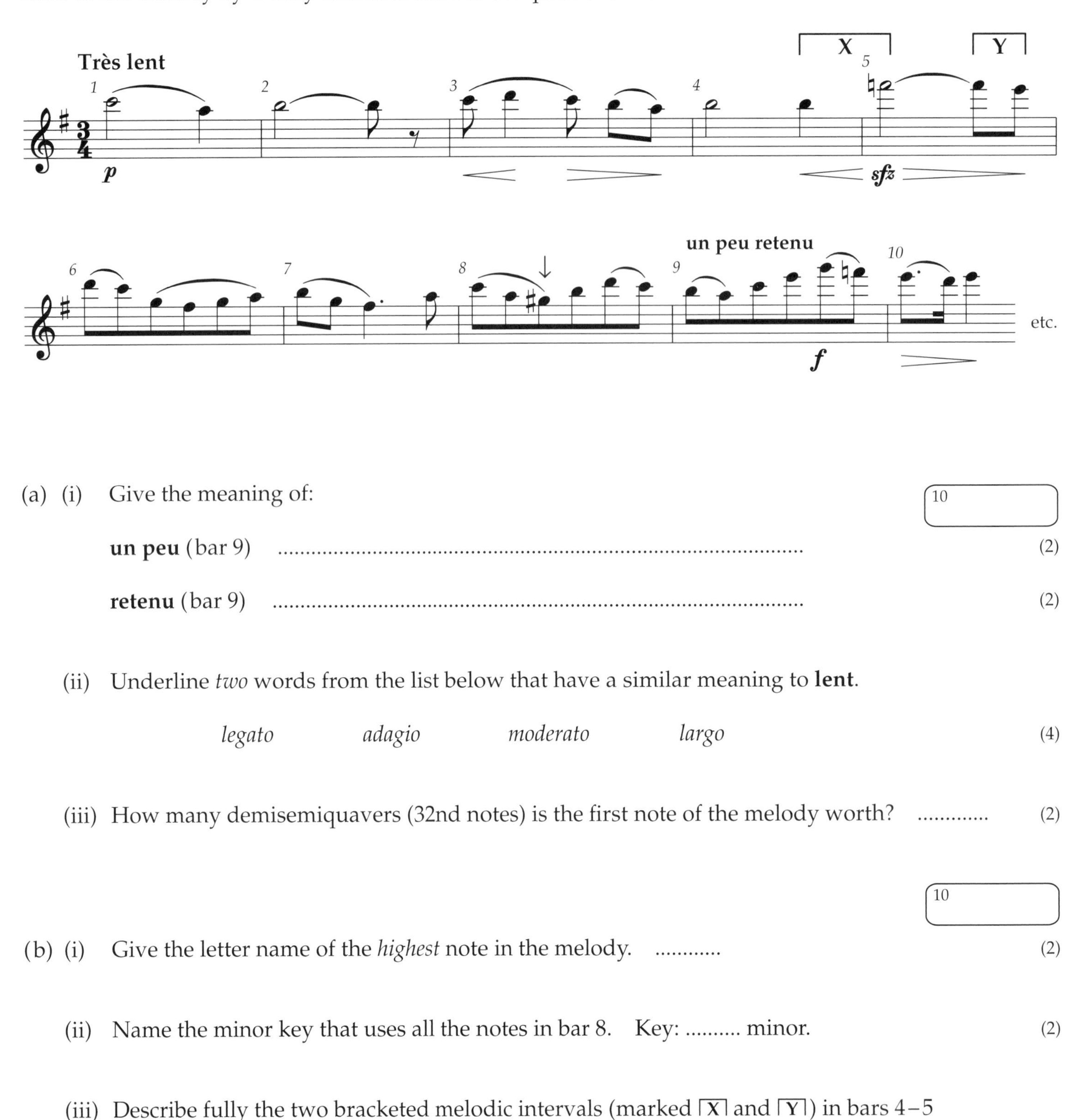

(a) (i) Give the meaning of:

10

un peu (bar 9) .... (2)

retenu (bar 9) .... (2)

(ii) Underline *two* words from the list below that have a similar meaning to **lent**.

legato *adagio* *moderato* *largo* (4)

(iii) How many demisemiquavers (32nd notes) is the first note of the melody worth? .... (2)

10

(b) (i) Give the letter name of the *highest* note in the melody. .... (2)

(ii) Name the minor key that uses all the notes in bar 8. Key: .... minor. (2)

(iii) Describe fully the two bracketed melodic intervals (marked X and Y) in bars 4–5 (e.g. major 3rd, perfect 4th).

X .... (2)

Y .... (2)

(iv) Write as a breve (double whole-note) an enharmonic equivalent of the note marked ↓ in bar 8.

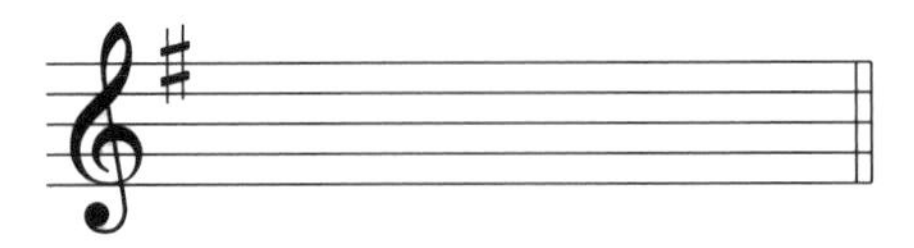

(2)

(c) (i) Complete the following statements: 10

The lowest-sounding member of the standard orchestral brass family is the .... (2)

The member of the standard orchestral string family that normally uses the alto clef is the .... (2)

(ii) Answer TRUE or FALSE to each of the following statements:

Violinists may sometimes be asked to play 'sul G'. .... (2)

A flautist may sometimes be asked to play 'pizzicato'. .... (2)

(iii) Name a standard orchestral percussion instrument that produces sounds of indefinite pitch. .... (2)

4 (a) Write one octave **ascending** of the scale of G♯ **melodic** minor. 10
Do *not* use a key signature but put in all necessary sharp or flat signs.
Use semibreves (whole notes) and begin on the tonic.

(b) Write one octave **descending** of the major scale that has this key signature.
Use semibreves (whole notes) and begin on the tonic.

5 (a) Rewrite this melody with the notes correctly grouped (beamed).

10

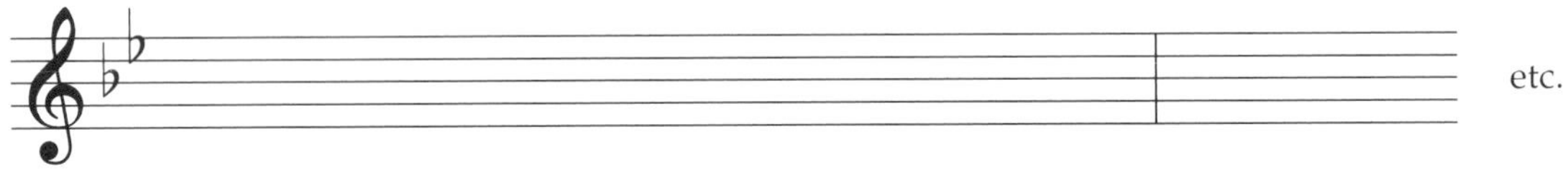

(b) Name the ornament in bar 3. ....

6 (a) Rewrite these alto clef notes at the same pitch but using the bass clef.

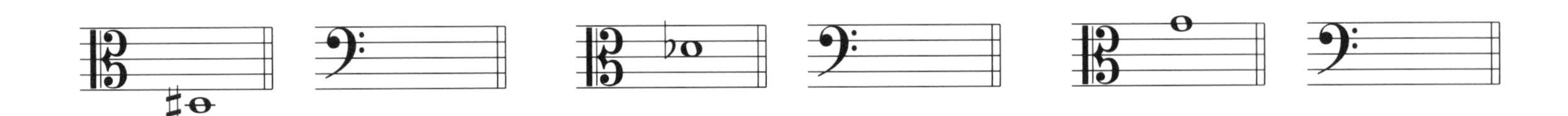

(b) Rewrite these treble clef notes at the same pitch but using the alto clef.

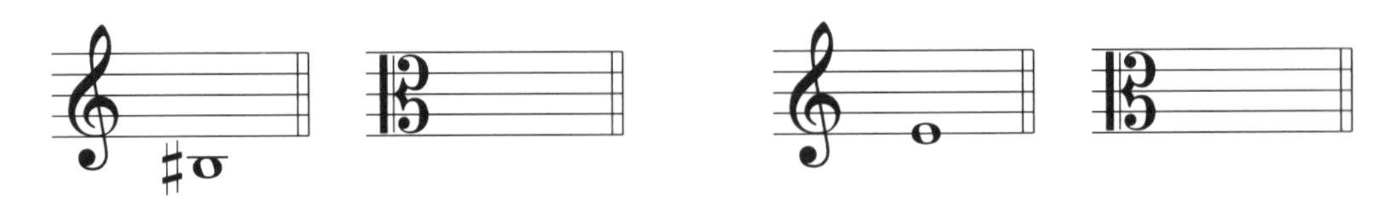

7 (a) Name each of the numbered chords as tonic (I), subdominant (IV) or dominant (V). The key is E major.

15

Chord:

(1) ....

(2) ....

(3) .... (9)

(b) Write the named triads as shown by the key signatures.

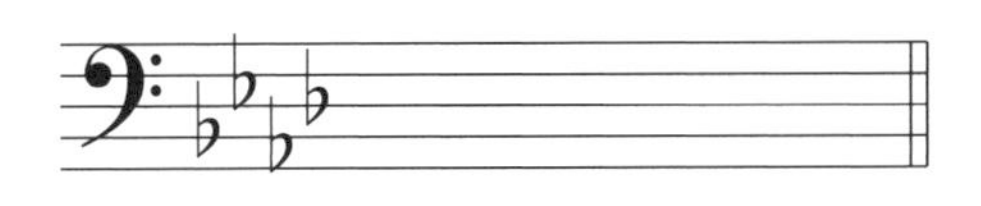

major key
tonic

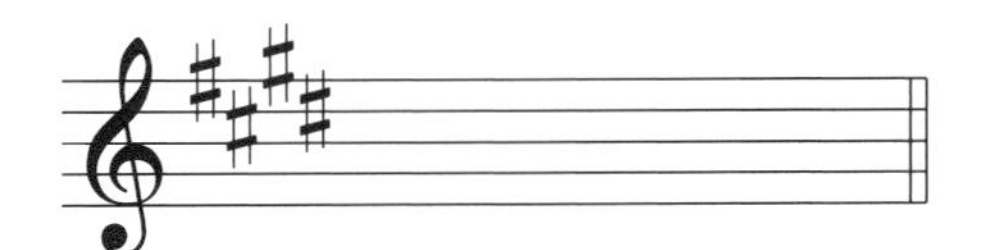

minor key
dominant

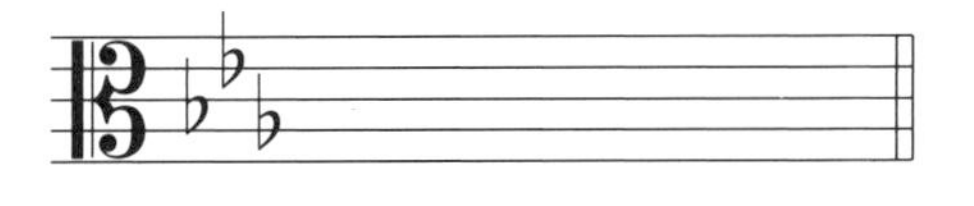

minor key
subdominant

(6)

Theory Paper Grade 4 2014 S

Duration 2 hours

This paper contains SEVEN questions, ALL of which should be answered.
Write your answers on this paper – no others will be accepted.
Answers must be written clearly and neatly – otherwise marks may be lost.

1 Look at this melody by Brahms and then answer the questions below. 15

Maestoso

ff tr tr etc.

(a) Give the meaning of **Maestoso**. .... (2)

(b) Describe the time signature as: simple or compound .... (1)

duple, triple or quadruple .... (1)

(c) Name one similarity and one difference between bar 3 and bar 5.

Similarity .... (1)

Difference .... (1)

(d) Draw a circle around two notes next to each other that are a minor 7th apart. (2)

(e) Rewrite the first two notes in bar 2 so that they sound at the same pitch, but using the alto clef. Remember to put in the key signature.

(3)

(f) Give the number of a bar which contains two notes with different letter names that are *not* in the key of D minor. Bar .... (2)

(g) A square bracket (⌐¬) has been drawn over the first phrase. Mark all the other phrases in the same way. (2)

2 EITHER 10

(a) Write a rhythm on one note, with time signature and bar-lines, to fit these words.
Write each syllable under the note or notes to which it applies.

Loveliest of trees, the cherry now
Is hung with bloom along the bough. *A. E. Housman*

Rhythm ____

Words ....

Rhythm ____

Words ....

OR

(b) Write a complete four-bar rhythm in $\frac{3}{2}$ time using the given opening.

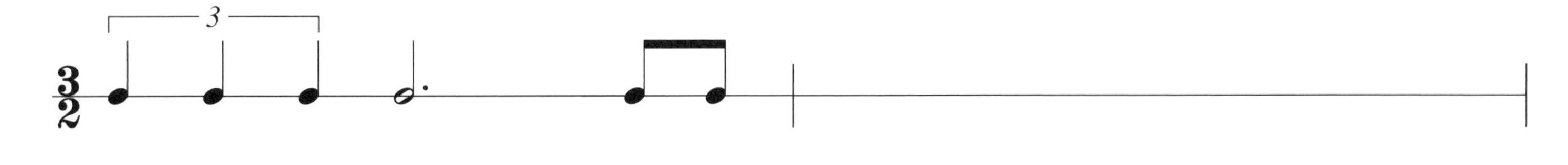

3 Look at this melody by Gurlitt and then answer the questions that follow.

Allegretto scherzando

p leggiero

(a) (i) Give the meaning of:

10

Allegretto scherzando .... (4)

leggiero .... (2)

(ii) Draw a bracket (⎣______⎦) under four notes next to each other that form part of a chromatic scale. (2)

(iii) Write as a breve (double whole-note) an enharmonic equivalent of the first note in bar 2. (2)

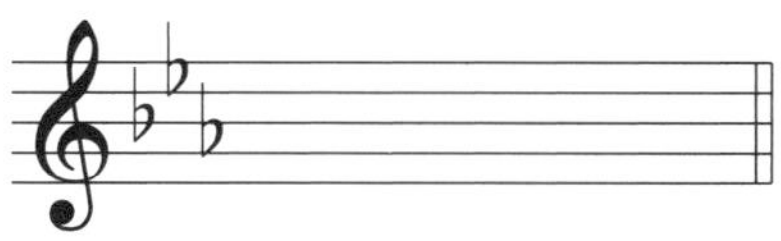

10

(b) (i) The key of the melody is C minor. Give the number of a bar which contains the submediant note of this key. Bar .... (2)

(ii) Which other key has the same key signature as C minor? .... (2)

(iii) In how many bars can *all* the notes of the tonic triad of C minor be found? .... (2)

(iv) Answer TRUE or FALSE to each of the following statements:

Bars 5–8 have the same pitches as bars 1–4 apart from two notes. .... (2)

All the melodic intervals in bar 3 are perfect intervals. .... (2)

(c) (i) Name a standard orchestral string instrument, which normally uses the treble clef, that could play this melody so that it sounds at the same pitch.

10

.... (2)

(ii) Which member of the standard orchestral string family normally uses the alto clef? .... (2)

(iii) Name the highest-sounding member of the standard orchestral woodwind family. .... (2)

(iv) Underline *two* instruments from the list below that are members of the standard orchestral percussion family.

timpani violin oboe bass drum (4)

4 (a) Write one octave **ascending** of the scale of B♭ **harmonic** minor. Do *not* use a key signature but put in all necessary sharp or flat signs. Use semibreves (whole notes) and begin on the tonic.

10

(b) Add all necessary sharp, flat or natural signs to the notes that need them to make a chromatic scale beginning on the given note.

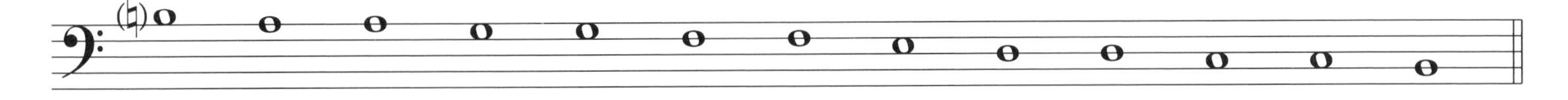

5 This melody by Albinoni contains *five* deliberate mistakes.
Rewrite it correctly on the blank stave below.

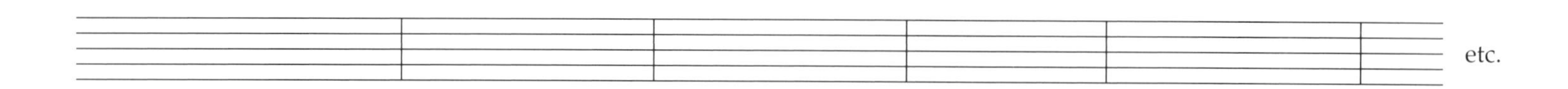

6 Name each of these notes, as shown in the first answer.

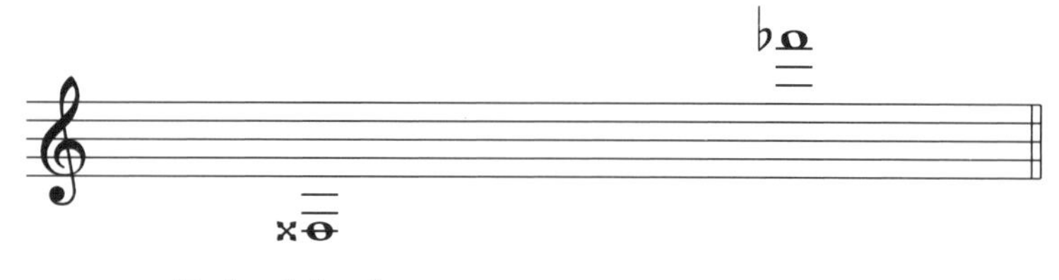

F double sharp ....

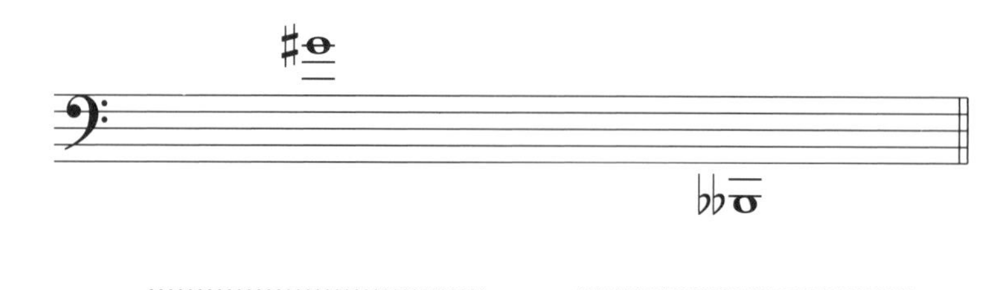

....

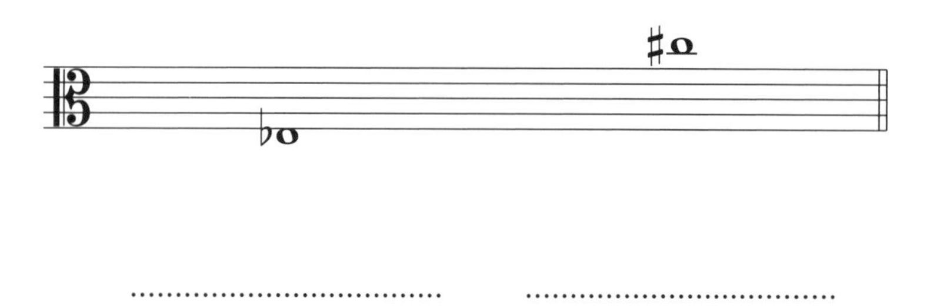

....

7 (a) Name each of the numbered chords as tonic (I), subdominant (IV) or dominant (V). The key is G major.

15

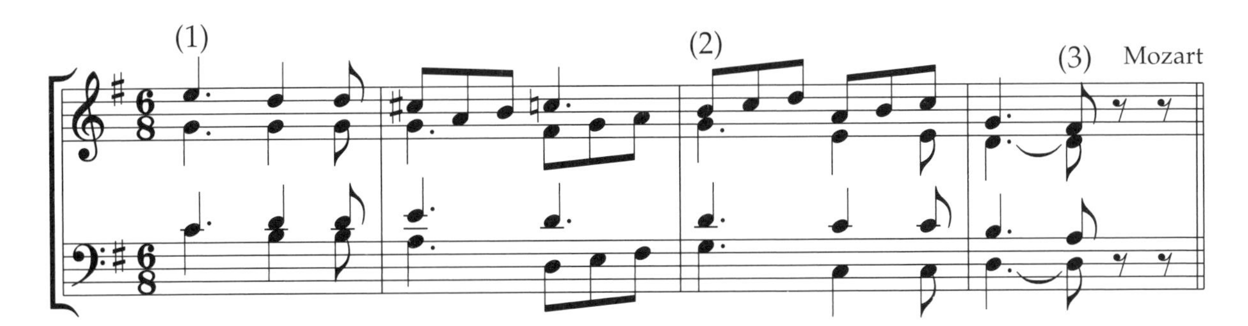

Chord:

(1) ....

(2) ....

(3) .... (9)

(b) Write the named triads as shown by the key signatures.

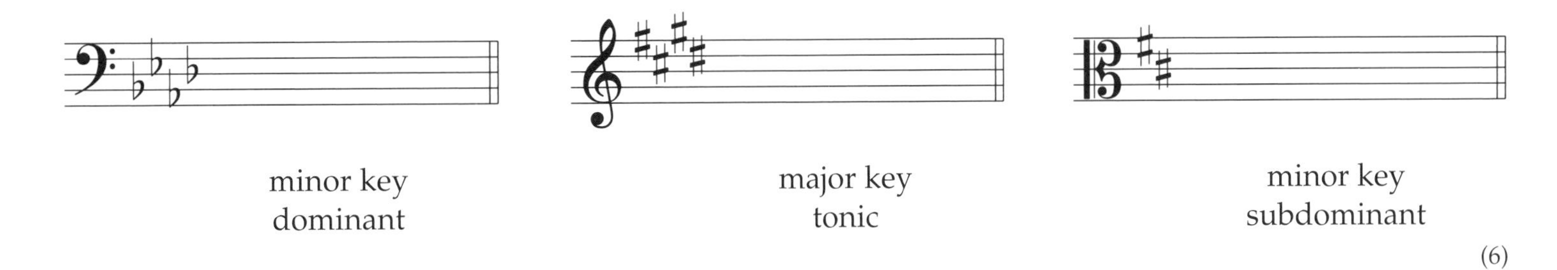

minor key dominant

major key tonic

minor key subdominant

(6)